Presents

D1454091

DISCOVERING

Culture and Values

A collection of texts

to accompany

Steps to Discovering
Culture and Values

KARINA YOUNK

Art Image Publications

Thoughtsteps is an intermediate learning resource based on the integration of language arts, science, and social studies, along with other subject areas and processing skills, whenever there are natural links. *Thoughtsteps* can be used with the entire class, with small groups, with individual students, or as a learning centre.

EDITORS
Joan Irving
Catherine Stewart
André Vandal

STUDENT EDITORS
Alexandre Fallon
Shannon Provencher

ILLUSTRATORS
François Thisdale
Richard Poissant
Mohamed Danawi
Stéphane Jorisch
Pierre Massé

PILOT CLASSES
Donna Anderson, Grade 6/7
Mount Benson Elementary, Nanaimo, BC

Paul Chetty, Grade 7/8
Miskooseepi School, Blood Vein River, MB

CONSULTANTS IN MUSIC, ART, AND LITERATURE
Sue Postans, Nanaimo, BC
Regan Rasmussen, Victoria, BC
Linda Irvine, Nanaimo, BC
Donna Klockars, Nanaimo, BC

ISBN: 1-896876-19-6

CANADA
Beauchemin Publishing Group/Art Image Publications Inc.
3281 Jean-Beraud Avenue
Laval, QC
H7T 2L2

Tel: (514) 334-5912
     1 800 361-2598
Fax: 1 800 559-2598

USA
Art Image Publications, Inc.
P.O. Box 568
Champlain, NY 12919
Tel: 1 800 361-2598
Fax: 1 800 559-2598

Printed in Canada

Table of Contents

Beyond Folklore

Beautiful Noise

A World of Legends

Beyond Folklore

Long Ago

Long ago, we came
from faraway lands
to struggle
in this land of snow.

Time passed, we strove,
amidst anguish and joy,
to adapt
in this newborn land.

We learned
with the help of friends
to feel safe
in this land of warmth.

Today, we dream
of a bright future
and success
in this land of hope.

Forever, we strive
to follow our ancestors
as we build
this land of our dreams.

K. Younk

The Journey

Inuit, first peoples of the North,
once trekked far from an eastern home
through ice, shifting snow, raging waters
in their search for a better life.

Asia... Bering... Arctic... Canada,
names unknown to the Inuit
as they settled into their new homes,
still searching for a better life.

The Inuit journey winds onward,
weaving its rugged trail of change,
through the bustling paths of newcomers,
each searching for a better life.

Inuit dreams of a better life
in this land of ages ago
guide them along rugged trails of change
and carve their paths to the future.

K. Younk

And This Was the Traditional Way of Life

Arctic
great white desert
endless cliffs, icy fjords,
roaring ice floes, silent tundra,
Our Home.

Please, husky sled dogs
help me trudge safely along
winter's icy paths

In the Arctic days
life and death is a matter
of thick, warm clothing.

Igloo
a warm shelter
during long, frozen winters
battered by wild Arctic winds
of home.

Poems by **Jean Pruneau**

Sun
season
shining bright
trap, fish, hunt, spear
seal, trout, caribou, bear, whale
food, clothes, tools, homes
sunny, warm
summer
days

Our
clothing
supple, warm
tan, dry, chew, shape
parkas, mitts, mukluks
cut, stitch, adorn
bright, new garb
mother
made

Poems by Jean Pruneau

Changes

Cold winds blow
    in the Arctic still
While snow upon snow
    gathers and builds
Forming new drifts
    while shifting the old
Always changing
    seemingly unchanged.

The Inuit conquered cold
    built ice homes
While snow is a constant
    the winds have changed
Igloos have melted
    pre-fab homes emerged
Always changing
    seemingly unchanged.

The people struggled
    hunted for food
Where land is the provider
    order prevails
Wild bounty replaced
    by whiteman's store
Always changing
    seemingly unchanged.

Evenings were filled
    with legend and song
Where snow formed a culture
    proud and strong
TVs entertain now
    old ways are lost
Always changing
    seemingly unchanged.

Catherine Stewart

Changes, too

The climate has scarcely changed
but the Inuit have adapted
in a hostile, hardened world
where treasures lie frozen in snow.

Great changes crept slowly, unseen
welcoming pale people bearing gifts
offering to trade tradition for progress;
this was only the beginning.

The snowmobile's conveyor belt
gnaws at the tracks of the dogsled
woodstoves, electric heat in wooden homes
melt the memories of ice block shelters.

The Inuit huddle together
near hospital, school, church
garage and general store;
behold the benefits of their trades.

As the winds of change whip the North
the Inuit search for the treasured key
to unlock the doors of their past
inside their homes for the future.

K. Younk

A Treasured Heritage

Outside, it was still dark. Jonathan lay in his bed, his eyes wide open. He was waiting impatiently for the sun to come over the hills. Today was the day that he was to go fishing with his grandfather, the chief of the band.

He glanced over at his equipment for a third time, to be certain that it was all there. As he did, he heard the morning songs of the first birds. Running quickly outside, Jonathan looked at the eastern sky. There it was, a great yellow face peering over the hill as if it were hesitant to wake Mother Earth's creatures too abruptly.

Jonathan ran on to Bear Falls. An old man was sitting beneath a poplar tree close to the water's edge, his long silvery-white hair flowing over his square shoulders like water over the falls. An eagle feather hung from his beaded headband. This was Jonathan's grandfather, the chief of the band. Jonathan sat down quietly at the chief's side, waiting for his grandfather to speak first. As he listened to the flow of the falls, his earlier impatience disappeared, leaving him feeling peaceful and relaxed.

The chief got up. He opened his arms wide as if to embrace the whole sky and

he said, "Thank you, Sun." Then he looked down at his grandson's bag and smiled. "Jonathan, we're only going for the day… not for a whole week…! Are you sure you can carry all that? …Let's get started."

And so the two of them set off on their fishing trip. They soon approached a small stream. Jonathan had to set a rock in the middle of the stream so he could cross without falling in. He had no desire to carry a wet bag. It was already heavy enough!

"Tell me, Jonathan, did your rock stop the flow of the stream?"

"No, Grandfather. Look, the water runs around it."

The chief went on talking as they walked through the woods, "Our people are strong like the water in this stream. We are not stopped by obstacles, just like the water is not stopped by the rock."

Jonathan stopped in a clearing where raspberries were growing wild. A few red berries were visible under the prickly bushes.

The chief looked at Jonathan's outstretched fingers and whispered, "Never take all the fruit from a tree or all the berries from a bush. An insect, a bird, or a deer might pass here after you and might need the food, too."

Once the two adventurers reached Eagle's Bay, they cast their fishing lines

into the deep, green water and settled themselves comfortably on the warm rocks at the water's edge.

Jonathan's grandfather started to tell one of his stories to Jonathan. "One day, my father caught me spearing a salmon just for the challenge of spearing it. In his deep, stern voice he scolded me, 'My son, the Great Spirit has given you these fish so that they will be your brothers and so that they will nourish you when you are hungry. You must respect them and you must never hurt them for your pleasure, simply to show you are stronger.'"

Jonathan thought to himself, "Oh, Great Spirit, thank you for having given me my grandfather. His words are like autumn leaves that turn into rich, dark earth. So many of my friends don't even get to see their grandparents. I'm lucky to have Grandfather and to be so close to him." Turning to face the old chief, Jonathan asked, "Grandfather, tell me about the earth and the people of this land."

"My own grandfather's home was 30 metres long. All of his children lived under the roof of this big house. The rooms were divided only by blankets. An open fire in the middle of the big house served everyone's needs. The children were surrounded by aunts, uncles, and cousins who loved and protected them. Nobody really owned anything. Everything was shared."

Jonathan continued to ask questions, "Grandfather, sometimes I see people cutting down the trees on the mountains. I see them tearing the rich minerals from the earth's crust. Our Mother Earth took millions of years to craft these treasures. And then I see people throwing garbage into the rivers and toxic gases into the air. What will happen to the people on this earth?"

"Our brothers in the big cities have produced many important inventions," the chief answered. "These people are intelligent, powerful, and ambitious and have done much to develop what surrounds them to meet the needs of people. But it is most important to listen to what Nature has to say, Jonathan. Listen to your heart and to your love of Nature. Listen to Nature when you decide which is the best path to take to rebuild a strong and beautiful earth. Sometimes in our hurry to change things for the better, we have forgotten to ask Nature if she agrees that what seems best for people is also best for her other children."

"Grandfather, if I ever have children, will there still be wild berries for them to eat? Will I have the knowledge to show them how to use the roots of plants?

Will they laugh at me when I ask them to sing to their brothers, the salmon? I so wish that your peace amulet could bring true peace between the People of Earth and Nature."

Jonathan's grandfather looked softly down on Jonathan as he answered, "I see the faces of my people, the sons of your sons, the daughters of your daughters, their laughter filling the air. Peace and beauty will come back to our Mother Earth. The tools we will use to rebuild our people will be different. I see all of our brothers working together to renew their bonds with Nature. It is wonderful to live! It is also wonderful to die!…"

The chief stopped speaking. He pulled the feather from his headband and solemnly offered it to Jonathan. It wasn't necessary for either of them to speak. Jonathan understood. He felt the power and force of the eagle gliding into his heart. He was ready. He felt strong.
He was not afraid.

Shapes of Unity

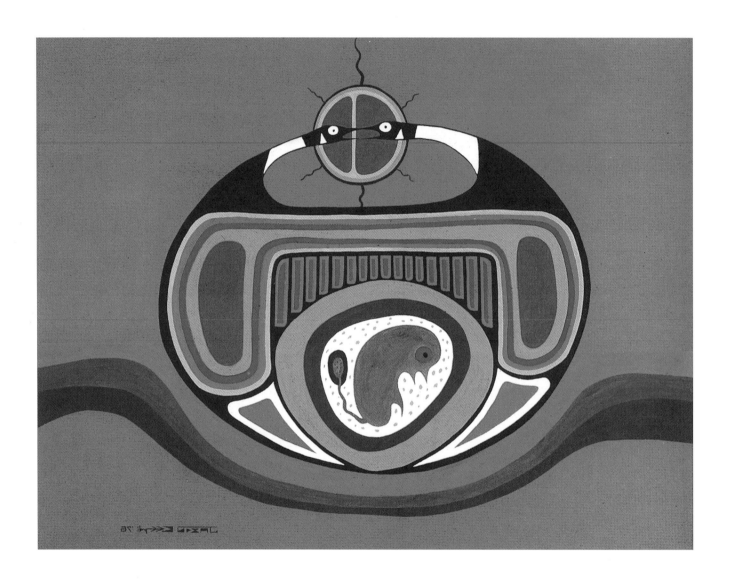

Rebirth

Jackson Beardy (1944-1984)

Jackson Beardy was an artist of the Cree nation in Manitoba. His art relates the legends that were told to him by his grandmother and his elders during his childhood. Beardy was especially interested in describing how life began, how life changes, how it is transformed, and how all forms of life are interdependent.

The Wolf Mask

Art Thompson (1948-)

Art Thompson is a West Coast artist of the Nuu Chah Nulth (Nootka) people. Both his father and his grandfather were carvers and made totem poles, masks, and finely crafted canoes. This mask represents a wolf. According to Nuu Chah Nulth legend, the wolf was reincarnated as a killer whale (an orca) because the wolf lives in family groups (packs) like the killer whale, which lives in pods. Sometimes the wolf is represented as a marine animal having the same qualities as the killer whale.

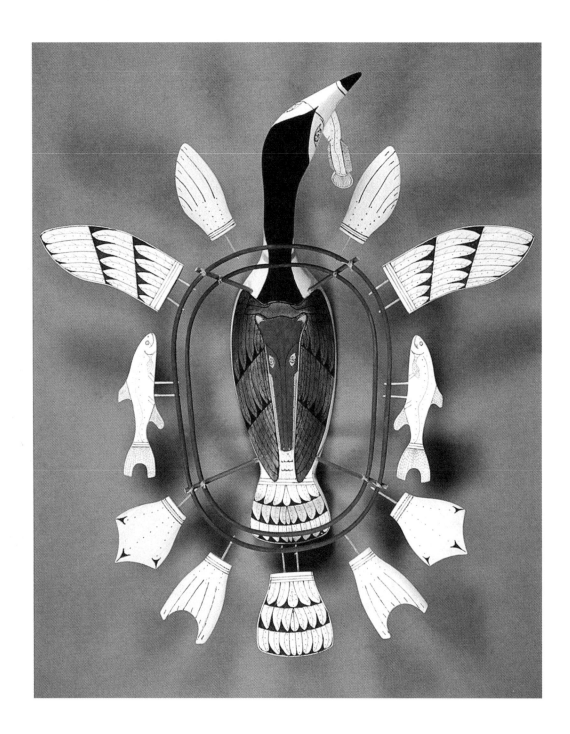

The Loon Mask

Edward Kiokan (1903-)

This mask was constructed by Edward Kiokan, an Eskimo artist from Nunivak Island in Alaska. A circle forms the support for the mask. This circle represents unity and protection. It also symbolizes the planets as they revolve around the sun. Attached to the circle are fish and wings. The fish represent the loon's source of food. The wings represent the loon's ability to fly through the skies. This mask is meant for display rather than for ceremonial purposes.

The Spirit of the Sea Mammal

The maker of this mask is unknown, though it is thought to have been made around 1885. This type of mask was worn during traditional dances. The First Nations peoples also wore these masks to tell a story or to sing a song about an aspect of their life. It is believed that this mask represents the spirit of an Arctic sea mammal. In Alaskan First Nations cultures, the mask was a way of making the unseen world of magic and spirits become visible.

Beautiful Noise

Cherished Cultures

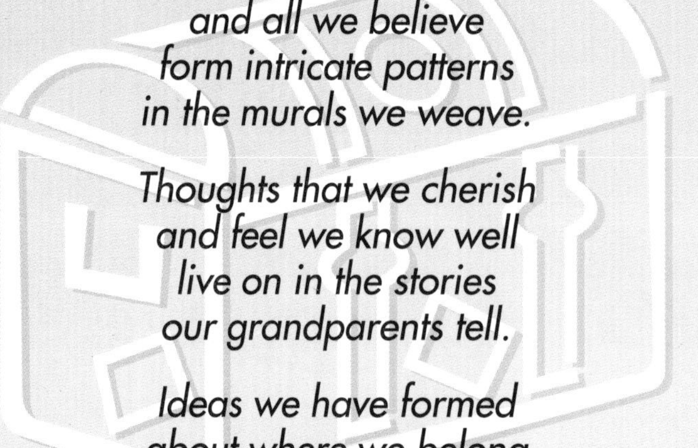

That which we value,
and all we believe
form intricate patterns
in the murals we weave.

Thoughts that we cherish
and feel we know well
live on in the stories
our grandparents tell.

Ideas we have formed
about where we belong
pass on to children
through music and song.

The roots of our past
give strength to our ways
creating a future
for new yesterdays.

K. Younk

Did You Know That...

History books used to state that Canada was "discovered" in 1534. Perhaps some people didn't discover Canada's beauty until then, but others had known of it long before. Bretons had fished off the coasts of Labrador and Newfoundland for centuries. The Vikings had tried to establish a settlement in northern Newfoundland a thousand years earlier. And before Canada was "discovered" by any of these European groups, it had long been the home of First Nations peoples with tales of their own to tell.

The numerous First Nations groups living in Canada continue to tell their stories in more than 50 different languages and many more dialects. Yet, everywhere on this planet, populations are changing and Canada is no exception. Today, Canada's cities and communities are a mosaic of people from many lands. Home to the First Nations peoples, over the past 500 years Canada has also welcomed people from all over the world. And for every person who comes to Canada, a new story is born – a story of hopes, dreams, and adventures.

The rich diversity of Canada's communities can only be truly understood when we stop to listen to the many exciting adventures people have had, to hear their tales of the past, their heritage, and their dreams for the future – for Canada.

Early Arrivals

Bigfoot Chief and Subordinates

Paul Kane (1810-1871)

Paul Kane was born in Ireland and came to Canada when he was nine. Paul Kane's works are looked upon as documentaries of the lives of First Nations peoples. The details in the costumes he painted are so precise as to provide an accurate reflection of how the First Nations people dressed during that period. As many of these traditions have disappeared, Paul Kane's art provides valuable insight into their way of life and ensures that they are not forgotten.

However, Kane's paintings cannot portray every aspect of First Nations culture. Without hearing the words and watching the daily actions of the people, many of the assumptions we make about people of the past are inaccurate or incomplete. These assumptions are often based on our own contemporary cultural perspectives. The early officials sent out from France or Britain to trade goods and to claim land for their countries kept journals not unlike the diaries of today's tourists. These government officials could not possibly record or even understand everything their native hosts tried to tell them.

Behind the Bonsecours Market, Montreal (1866)

William Raphaël (1833-1914)

William Raphaël was born in Prussia in 1833 to a Jewish family. He studied art in Berlin. In 1857, at the age of 25, he emigrated from Germany to New York. Three years later, Raphaël moved to Montreal, where he lived for the remainder of his life. During this period, he earned his livelihood by painting portraits. The invention of photography destroyed his market for lifelike paintings. Instead, he turned to painting Canadian scenes and thus became one of Canada's most popular artists.

When late 19th-century immigrants arrived in Canada by ship from Europe, they would land in Halifax, Quebec City, Montreal, and other port cities. But the journey usually did not end there. The railway would then deliver these weary travellers to their final destinations. Homesteads, villages, and cities began to appear wherever Canada's new railway could take them.

At the same time, in British Columbia, settlers were arriving from the States and from Asia in search of either quick riches in gold-panning or hard-earned wages in mining, logging, and fishing. They, too, struggled to lay down tracks through B.C.'s mountainous terrain.

Finally, in November of 1885, Canada's dreamed-of National Railway was completed. The nation was open for travel from coast to coast.

Potato Picking (1936)

Jean Palardy (1905-1991)

Jean Palardy was born in Fitchburg, Massachusetts. His Canadian parents decided to return to Canada when Jean was three. Palardy studied and took up painting. He became interested in landscapes early in his career. After meeting the renowned historian, Marius Barbeau, Palardy began to collect Quebec folksongs, traditional legends, and art. These became his inspiration. His paintings contain so many details on rural life and customs that they are valuable historical records of the farming communities in Quebec in the early 1900s.

During Palardy's time, the Canadian government encouraged selected groups of immigrants to come to Canada to farm the land. British, Scottish, Irish, French, and American families filled Ontario and southern Quebec. Mennonite, Hutterite, and Ukrainian immigrants took up grain farming in the Prairies. Chinese, Japanese, and other Asian newcomers became avid produce farmers in B.C.'s lower mainland communities.

The Canadian landscape we know today was cultivated with the dreams and visions of these early settlers.

Monday, Washing Day

Miyuki Tanobe (1939 -)

Miyuki Tanobe was born and raised in Japan. In 1971, she moved to Montreal to marry Maurice Savignac. Miyuki brought with her the technique, *nihonga*, learned during her university studies in Japan. Paintings using this technique are generally done on rice paper. A special paintbrush is used to apply a mixture of powdered paints, *souni* (a black ink), glue, and water. Sand and other minerals are often added to the paint mixture to adjust the texture of the colours.

Though Miyuki Tanobe's technique is Japanese, the subjects of her paintings are definitely Canadian. Many of her paintings, like this one, depict the joys of life in the working-class residential areas of Montreal. *Lundi, jour de lessive* ("Monday, Washing Day") brings alive the small backyard meeting place where children gather to have fun and where parents often chat with their neighbours.

Canada's communities continue to grow and to thrive as new immigrants bring with them memories of the past and dreams for their future.

Discovering Freedom

They dreamed
from their comfortable,
civilized, sheltered world
of new hopes, a new land, a new start
utopia.

They came
tossed by seas, rugged waves
onto Canada's shores
and were met by the wild rocky soils
uncertainty.

They lived
needs unmet, cold,
hungry, scantily clad
as they built, piece by piece,
sparse shelters
first comforts.

They learned
to find warmth,
to grow strong, to flourish
kinships formed, cities rose,
life blossomed
society.

We strive
to grow up from
the seeds that they sowed
to honour their struggles,
hard labours
freedoms won.

C. Stewart

Where Are We Off To Now?

"Hey! Jesse! Elyssa! Come down to the kitchen! Hurry! I have some incredible news to tell you!"

Jesse gently laid his violin on his bed and headed for the door. As he descended the stairs, he thought about what his dad might have dreamed up this time. It would be something out of the ordinary, for Dad always had great ideas.

Elyssa dropped her astronaut book on the floor and raced from her room. She pushed past her brother so that she could be the first down the stairs. The excitement in her father's voice reminded her of the time, three years ago, when they had decided to take a family cycling trip. For three weeks, this amazing journey had taken them through remote corners of the Maritimes. What a memorable experience it had been! Now Elyssa was curious to know what Dad was so excited about.

She burst through the kitchen door ahead of her brother, trying not to shout as she breathlessly asked, "What's going on, Dad?"

"Sit down, both of you. I have something to show you." He slapped a picture down on the table in front of them.

Both children stared at the picture in silent disbelief. They looked at each other first to check that their reaction was the same. Then they turned their worried expressions to their dad. "You made us race down here to show us a picture of a battered old van?"

"Yes!" their dad replied excitedly. He didn't even notice that his children were beginning to wonder if he had lost his sanity.

"So what's so special about this old toaster?"

"In exactly one month, my dear partners, this will be our home! We're going on a trans-Canada trip this summer!"

"What? Are you serious? For the whole summer?"

"Yes, kids! So what do you think? We'll travel like we did three years ago. No housecleaning, no gardening, no renovations, no routine… We'll follow our noses, our whims, and go wherever the roads take us."

"Yippee!"

"Wow, this is rad!"

"Just wait until I tell my friends. They'll be so jealous!"

Jesse looked up at his dad, his eyes sparkling with ideas. "Dad, since we won't be on a bicycle this time, may I bring my violin along?"

"Of course, Jesse. You can play for us during the entire trip if you like."

"No way!" said Elyssa, "Not during the whole trip. I'll never be able to concentrate on the inventions and discoveries in my books! And this time, I intend to bring lots and lots of books!" Elyssa remembered all too well the bicycle trip where her only reading material consisted of road maps and her trip diary.

"Now wait just a minute! The van may have a little more space than the bicycles… but we have to be able to live in it, too. The two benches on each side of the table will be used as seats during the day and a bed at night. The compartments inside the benches are your storage spaces. Everything that you want to bring along will have to fit in there. So you'll need to think carefully about what you're bringing."

"This will be almost like the astronauts in their space shuttle!" exclaimed Elyssa.

Jesse looked at his sister and grinned. "Earth calling Elyssa! Imagine my sister, the explorer, off to meet every inventor in the country. Then there's me; I can't think of anything else but the early settlers who filled their evenings with singing, dancing, and music. It's like we were born on two different planets."

Their dad smiled, "I hope my arms will be long enough to hold the two of you down to the van."

Elyssa burst into laughter, "Right, Dad! I can see you now with your extensible arms just like the CANADARM and your dancing feet. You'll look hilarious!"

"Enough of your crazy ideas! I've got to run to the office to make some calls. If I want to take an extended vacation this summer, I've still got a lot of overtime hours to put in. While I'm gone, maybe you could start thinking about where we should stop during our trip."

"OK, Dad. And we've also got plans to make about what we want to bring. That may take us the next three weeks. Thanks for the wonderful news! Now get to work! We've got things to do. Don't worry about supper, Dad, we'll make it!"

Two days later, when Dad called from the office to say he would be late, he added, "Have you thought about our vacation?"

"That's all we've thought about," answered Jesse. "I didn't realize how much there was to organize and how many places there are to see."

"Yes," replied Dad, "Have you both chosen the sites you wish to visit? I made a list of the art galleries in the major cities, as well as the names of the artists on exhibit in each one. From there, I chose the ones that we will visit."

"Oh, no, Dad! Do we really have to visit art galleries?" Elyssa remembered their last visit to an artist's exhibit. Her father had studied every painting for what seemed like hours.

"Let's make a deal, Elyssa," her father responded. "You come to the galleries with me, because I will be going to all of your choices with you. I can tell you a little about the artist's techniques and his or her lifestyle. It will be an art appreciation lesson. You don't have to study the art as long as I do. You can bring a book to read when you're done."

"Okay, Dad. I guess on a trip like this we have to compromise because each of us will want to see different things. I've picked out which museums seem most interesting. Maybe in the Space Sciences Centre in Edmonton, I will give you a lesson!"

"What about you, Jesse?" asked Dad. "Where do you want to go?"

"Well, I've got three favourites. I want to visit the Plains of Abraham. Battles were fought there. It must be an exciting place. Then, I want to see Fort Garry. It is an authentic fort with actors re-enacting the early settlers' lives. My most exciting choice is Drumheller, Alberta. Did you know that dinosaurs once lived there? Imagine standing where those mammoth creatures once stood."

"Okay, kids, I'm glad you've done your research. Tonight, when I get home, we'll take a look at what you plan on bringing. Bye for now!"

A World of Legends

Shared Secrets

Tell me your people's creation story
so that I may discover
if your people are friendly or fierce,
if they will share with or overpower my people.

Tell me your most valued legends
so that I may understand
who you are, what you cherish
and where our paths may coincide.

Listen to my people's creation story
so that you and I may know
if you are able to accept my ways
and to learn from me as I learn from you.

Listen to my most valued legends
so that I may observe
your reactions to my secrets shared
in the hopes of becoming your trusted friend.

K. Younk

Tell Me a Tale!

"I'm ready for my story, Papa!" Alexander called from his bed.

"Did you brush your teeth, Ali?" his father questioned. Ali was a nickname that had been given to Alexander when he was two years old. At that time, he wasn't able to say his whole name, so he had tried to say Alex. But Alex came out sounding like Ali, so his father had nicknamed him Ali.

"Yes, Papa. I even put all my toys away in the box."

"Wonderful! I'm on my way."

"Which story will you tell me tonight, Papa?"

"This evening, Ali, I'm not going to read you a story. I'm going…"

"But, Papa, you promised!"

"Wait! Let me finish! I'll keep my promise. Tonight, instead of reading you a story, I'll tell you a legend."

"But I don't want to hear a legend. I want one of your stories!"

"Do you know what a legend is?"

"No… but it must be something very boring."

"Did you know that legends were told long before storybooks were invented?"

"Really?" Alexander was beginning to change his mind, but he was careful not to let his father see that he was curious.

"Before books were printed, people used legends to try to explain the past. There are legends told to answer almost every possible question. Why is the sky blue? Why does the sun rise in the east every morning? Why does the moon only show part of its face? How did life on Earth begin?"

"Are these legends true?"

"No one really knows for sure. We do know that legends were told to pass on the values and history of a cultural group."

"Tell me, Papa, are there still legends?"

"Not really. In our time, we tend to rely on science to explain the phenomena that we don't understand. There doesn't seem to be a need for legends anymore. Yet, it's fascinating to think that there might be answers different from what science tells us."

"Please, Papa, hurry and start your legend."

"Legends are not meant to be told quickly. So since it's already quite late, I'll tell you a very short one. This is a dream-time story told by the first peoples of Australia, known as the Aborigines. This dream-time story explains how the rains returned…"

"I'm not at all tired, Papa. You can tell me every legend you know!"

A long time ago, long before people inhabited the earth, there was a great drought. As there was no water to be found, all the animals were very thirsty and many were dying of dehydration. One day, Oumpah, an ancestor of the wild boar, was tunneling a hole in the ground with his tusks in search of a place to cool off. He started to shove away at a large stone. It took all his strength to move it, which only made him thirsty and more exhausted. Just as he was about to abandon the stubborn obstacle, a trickle of water seeped from beneath the stone. The water spread quickly over the dry ground, flowing into the baked cracks and refreshing the withered plants in its path. As if a messenger had blown his bugle, animals instinctively came running to quench their thirst at the small spring.

Oumpah was quick to act. He called out, "Listen carefully, my friends. I know that you are all very thirsty. But we cannot be greedy with the water that the ground has given. We need to conserve this water as long as possible and share it so that the plants may grow and we may live."

The animals knew that Oumpah's words were wise. They stopped gulping, contenting themselves with only small sips. That way, there would be water for them again tomorrow and the next day and the next…

However, the great serpent decided that she did not need the advice of some silly old boar. During the night, she slithered up to the spring and drank as much water as her greedy body could hold.

In fact, she drank so much water that her stomach became over-bloated and she died. The next morning, when the animals arrived at the spring, there wasn't a single drop of water left to drink. They found the serpent by the spring, but her spirit had left her stiffened body. The animals were outraged at the serpent, yet it was too late. Sadly, the animals turned their backs on the dried-up spring and headed for their own corner of parched earth.

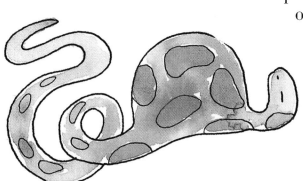

A few days later, three young koalas were playing in the dust near where the spring had been. Suddenly, they spotted several tiny snakes that had just hatched.

"Let's kill them! It was a snake who drank all our water. We don't want any more snakes around!"

From the sky, the spirit of the great serpent watched in anguish. When she saw her babies' pending fate, she started to cry. Teardrops slipped from her eyes and fell onto the little snakes below.

"Wait!" cried the kangaroo. "Water is falling from the sky to bless these little snakes.

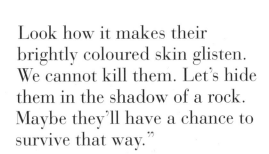

Look how it makes their brightly coloured skin glisten. We cannot kill them. Let's hide them in the shadow of a rock. Maybe they'll have a chance to survive that way."

Touched by the kangaroo's words, the great serpent's tears flowed freely. The rain was falling so heavily now that all the animals were getting wet. They danced for joy as the water rose in the lakes, streams, and rivers.

Seeing that her babies were safe, the great serpent arched her body in the sky. The colourful stripes on her skin shone in the sun, forming the first rainbow. The animals turned their gaze to the sky. What a sign for celebration!

"Well, my little Ali, did you like that legend? Ali?"

"Hum, mmm…"

Alexander didn't really answer for he was fast asleep. His dreams were about rain, rivers, and serpents. He could see the great serpent spirit in the sky arching her rainbow-coloured body over the land to take a small sip from the fresh waters she had sent to the earth.

Alexander's father gently rearranged the covers as he bent forward to kiss Alexander softly on the forehead. Returning to the living room, he smiled as he heard the pitter-patter of raindrops tapping against the window pane.

The Beginning of the World

A European Norse creation myth

In the beginning, there was nothing but an endless darkness. There were no lands, no seas, no welcoming breezes. To the north, a frozen emptiness filled the air with an icy fog. To the south, fire and flames lapped at the air. A river of ice flowed from the north and a sea of fire spread from the south. Where these two extremes met, the giant known as Ymir was born. From the sparks of fire and ice, the gods emerged. It would be their responsibility to guide the course of the planets and the stars.

From the body of the giant, Ymir, the earth was formed. His bones became the mountains. His teeth turned into the pebbles found at the seaside. His blood became the ocean which would give life to the earth. From Ymir's skull, the dome of the sky was created, held in the four corners by the dwarves named East, West, North, and South.

The earth was round and the sandy shores bathed in the deep waters of the ocean. It was an ideal place for the children of the gods to play. They would come down from the stars every day to romp in their own little paradise.

One morning, three of the gods' sons were walking along the seashore when they found two logs that had been abandoned by the waves. They picked up the logs and carved them into the shape of a woman and a man. Then each young god offered their new toys a present. The first god gave them life and soul, the second wisdom and spirit, and the third speech and reason. Then they clothed them and named them. The man was named Asir and the woman was called Embla.

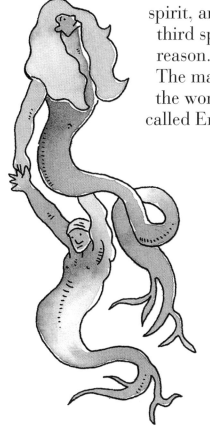

Asir and Embla's first child was a girl. Her hair was a shiny black and her skin was dark. Her parents named her Night.

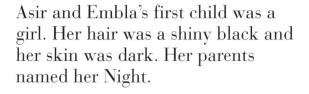

The gods, happy to see such a beautiful girl, offered her a husband with blond hair and fair skin. Night was delighted to marry the son of the gods', whose name was Day.

One day, when the gods needed help, they called on Asir and Embla to lend them their children, Day and Night. With her parents' permission, the young woman and her husband departed for the kingdom of the gods. However, they would not be alone in their journey for they now had two children, Sun and Moon.

The gods were so delighted with the births of the two children that they offered both Day and Night a horse and chariot to transport them and their children. Then, the gods sent the horses and their chariots high in the sky so that the proud parents could stroll around the earth with their children.

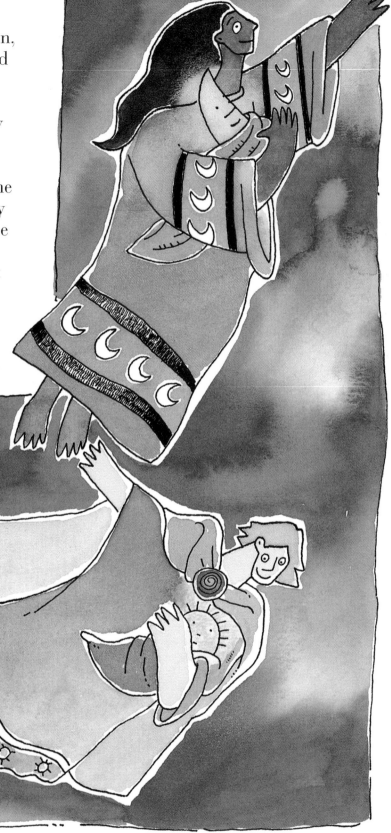

Thus Asir, Embla, and all of Night's sisters and brothers could admire the children at all times.

This is why Night would drive her horse, Frosty Mane, across the sky from dusk until dawn. In her arms, she held her daughter, Moon, who would occasionally peek out to show all or just a part of her glowing face. In the morning, the only traces left by the chariot were the dewdrops that had fallen from Frosty Mane's brow.

For his part, Day would illuminate the sky with the brilliant rays from his horse, Glistening Mane. His boy, Sun, would amuse himself by darting between the clouds to hide from his parents or his grandparents.

This is what the Vikings say about the beginning of our world.

And So the Night Was Born

A South American Tupi legend

In many mythical legends about the beginnings of our world, the earth was plunged into darkness. This Tupi legend from the Amazon jungle tells how darkness was returned to the earth.

Long, long ago, in the beginning of the world, the tiger and the serpent were archenemies. The serpent, dark in colour, represented the night. The tiger, glowing brightly, was the symbol for daylight. The two raged in a violent battle that was to last for millions of years.

Finally, the tiger won. To punish the serpent, the tiger locked him in a trunk. From this moment on, the earth basked in never-ending sunlight. The darkness was gone, imprisoned in the old trunk. With daylight as the permanent ruler, animals began to die. They were exhausted from hunting or from being hunted constantly, with never a moment to rest.

One day, the daughter of the Great Tiger made the decision to visit the earth to see what was happening in the land of constant light. She fell in love with a handsome native who lived in the depths of the Amazon forest. But the days without darkness were too much for her. Her eyes were blinded by the brightness of the sun's rays. She needed the night to rest her eyes and to be able to sleep.

So she told her husband, "Please go find my father, the Great Tiger. Ask him to send me the night so that I may rest again."

The good man felt he could not leave her side, so he called upon his three most faithful friends and asked them for help. "Go to the Great Tiger, in the brighter world far below the water. Tell him that his daughter will die if

she is not able to sleep. Ask him to set the night free."

In their canoe, the three faithful friends left in search of the Great Tiger in his kingdom below the water.

They found him at last, below the farthest depths of the water. "Your daughter is dying," they told the Great Tiger. "If you do not set the night free, your daughter will never be able to sleep and she will die."

Upon hearing these words, the Great Tiger took the trunk and gave it to the three paddlers. "Here is the trunk that contains the night. Only my daughter may open this trunk, no one else. You must place this trunk in my

daughter's hands and in her hands only.
Do not open the trunk yourselves!"

The three friends took the trunk and
climbed into their canoe. During their
return voyage, they could hear all
kinds of strange noises, scratching
sounds, and groaning coming from
the trunk. They became very curious
to know what was inside. Finally,
they decided to ignore the orders of
the Great Tiger and they opened the
trunk. The night fell quickly over
them, plunging them into darkness.
They were unable to see anything,
but all around them strange noises
filled the darkness.

In the forest, each twig turned into an
animal. On the trees, each leaf became
a bird. The pebbles in the streams were
transformed
into fish, the aquatic
plants into frogs and snakes. The forest calm was
invaded by the sounds of the animals.

The daughter of the Great Tiger could finally sleep. When
she awoke, she saw the canoe. In place of the three friends
were three monkeys who bounded from the canoe and
began to screech.

"You went against the Great Tiger's wishes," she said.
"You will now live in the forest and screech all you like,
but nobody will understand you." And so the daughter of
the Great Tiger took two balls of twine and changed
them into birds. As she freed the two birds, she
declared, "From this day forward, one bird will sing to
celebrate the coming of night and the other to
welcome the dawn. In this way, the creatures of the
earth will be able to live and sleep in peace."

The Legend of White Bison and the Sacred Pipe

A North American Lakota legend

It was during the period when there was very little food on the earth. The people of the plains were hungry. The elders decided to send the tribe's two best hunters in search of wild food. The two hunters set out on foot. They searched far and wide, but their search was in vain.

Finally, they decided to climb the highest hill to see if any animals were visible from there. They looked off into the western horizon and spied something coming toward them.

"What is it?" one of the young men asked.

"I don't know, but I do know that it is coming toward us," answered the other.

At first, they thought it was an animal. But as the form drew nearer, they realized that it was a woman. She was wearing the skin of a white bison and was carrying a beautiful scarf. Her movements were so smooth that she seemed to be floating above the ground.

The first hunter thought that she was a spirit from the heavens. His heart beat quickly with admiration. The second believed that she was a woman to be owned like an object. His mind was filled with evil ideas. As the woman approached them, the second tried to touch her. No sooner had he reached out, than thunder rumbled through the sky and a dark cloud hid him from view. When the cloud had vanished, only the skeleton of the hunter was left behind.

At this moment, the woman dressed in the skins of a white bison turned to address the first hunter, "Return to your people. Tell them that I bring good things. I bring a sacred object for your people, a message from the people of White Bison. Build a special meeting place for me in your village and I shall return in four days. Be sure to be ready!"

The young hunter did as the woman had asked. He returned to his people with the message from White Bison. Everyone set to work. A sacred spirit would visit their village. They hoped that they might be ready for her. Four days went by quickly, as they worked busily to build the special meeting lodge. On the fourth day, as promised, White Bison appeared on the horizon. In her hands she carried a shawl. The people invited her into the special lodge and offered her the place of honour. She untied her shawl and lifted the object it contained so that the people could look on the sacred pipe.

With her arms outstretched, White Bison held the pipe high and began to explain the importance of the symbolic pipe. "This pipe is made from red clay. The clay represents the skin and blood of our people and that of other peoples. The tube of the pipe symbolizes all the trees, all the plants, and everything that grows on this earth. The smoke which billows from the pipe is like the sacred winds that carry our prayers to Wakan Tanka, the Great Creator."

White Bison then showed them how to hold the pipe and how to offer it to the earth, the skies, and the four sacred winds. "This sacred pipe will show you the good ways. Follow it and it will lead you to the right paths. Now I must leave you, but we will meet again."

White Bison followed the path of the setting sun. The people watched in silence. Suddenly, White Bison threw herself down to the ground and rolled over once. When she got up again, she had become a black bison. She continued to follow the sun for a few more steps before lying down again. This time, she stood up as a brown bison. Again, she went on, and again she rolled over on the ground, rising up as a red bison. Finally, rolling in the earth for the fourth time, she stood up as White Bison and vanished over the horizon.

As soon as White Bison had disappeared in the glow of the setting sun, a herd of bison advanced on the village. The people were able to hunt again! The people knew then that as long as they would follow the good ways of the sacred pipe, they would live happily. They also knew that they were just one small part of something much greater and that, like the pipe, each small part depended on the other parts to form the whole. Everything belonged to the same universe.

43

Tokoyo's Courage

A Japanese folktale

Many, many years ago, Japan was ruled by the beloved Emperor Takatoki. However, a bizarre change had transformed the good emperor. His laws were now cruel and unjust. Poor Shima, a brave and faithful samurai warrior, was banished from Japan simply for asking a question of the emperor. His young daughter, Tokoyo, begged to go with her father to live on the Oki Islands, but her request was refused.

Thus Tokoyo remained in Japan. She earned her food and shelter by diving for oyster shells with the women of her village. Though she was much younger, she quickly learned to hold her breath longer and to dive deeper than all of the other women. Down in the deep water, Tokoyo's lonely tears could mix silently and unnoticed with the salt water.

At last, when Tokoyo could no longer bear to be alone, she made up her mind to search for her banished father. Asking the hardy fishermen to take her to the Oki Islands was of no use. Each would turn away, shuddering in fear of the emperor's rage. Discouraged, but unwilling to give up, Tokoyo crept down to the water's edge after the villagers had gone to bed. Stepping quietly into a small boat, she pushed off to tackle the treacherous sea alone.

Strong breezes and currents smiled at Tokoyo's determination. With the dawn, her feet were scrambling along the rocky beach of the desolate island. Seeing an old man hunting for food along the beach, Tokoyo eagerly begged him for news of her father.

The man's weather-beaten face became quite serious as he stared down at Tokoyo. "Little one, you are searching in vain. A wicked sea serpent holds your brave father captive in a cavern deep below this island. If the serpent should learn that you were here, he would surely kill you both."

Tokoyo, frightened and uncertain, listened to the kind traveller as he told her of how the emperor was ruling under the serpent's spell. After thanking the old fisherman, Tokoyo, her head bent, but her eyes burning with anger, returned to her small craft and pushed it slowly into the waves.

The old man, watching sadly from shore, started in surprise when he saw her small, frail body suddenly straighten up, pause for a moment, then dive into the crest of a wave.

Down, down Tokoyo plunged, her oyster knife clenched between her teeth, her eyes fixed on the dark as it rushed to meet her. Powerfully strange emotions were leading her directly to the serpent's cavern and to her father. Tokoyo winced as she looked upon her father's sleeping face seemingly frozen with painful sadness and his stiff body wrapped in sinews of seaweed.

Fearing that she had come too late, Tokoyo used her knife to cut through the bonds which held her father. Using the strong, sharp strokes she had often used to pry open oysters, she soon set her father free. But at that same moment, a sudden flash pierced the dark. The gleaming eyes of the sea serpent slithered angrily towards the reunited pair. Tokoyo, furious, darted forward, thrusting her knife into one of the glaring eyes. The shocked sea monster turned to retreat, but Tokoyo was quick to lunge again, this time for the beast's heart. The monstrous beast heaved and writhed furiously as it plummeted to its death in the depths below.

Moments later, a very astonished old man, still standing sadly on the shore, witnessed a sight that he would never grow weary of retelling. For there, out of the waves where Tokoyo had plunged only moments before, a proud samurai emerged. With a few swift strokes, Shima had carried his exhausted daughter Tokoyo to shore. The serpent's spells were broken and the emperor, upon hearing the old man's story, was quick to revoke the law that had banished his most faithful samurai.

Be Patient with the Lion

A Somali folktale from Ethiopia

Bizunesh had gladly married Gudina. However, Gudina's son, Segab, was not as delighted to have a new mother. No matter what Bizunesh did, or said, to show her love for Segab, the young boy would rebel. When she made him beautiful clothes, he played in the dirt until they were soiled and torn. When she offered to help him, he would turn away. When Segab was upset, Bizunesh would try to hold him to comfort him. He would only glare at her and run away. Gudina loved his new wife, but he could find no way to change Segab's ways.

Out of desperation, Bizunesh sought help from a wise man who lived in the hills. "Please, you must help me. I must have a love potion so that Segab will love me as I try to love him."

The wise man nodded his head. "Yes, I will help you when you bring me three whiskers from the chin of the lion."

"But that's an impossible task!"

"Perhaps, but if you truly love Segab, you will find a way."

Bizunesh went away, disappointed, but determined to try. She was extremely afraid of the lion. Fulfilling the task would not be easy. For days, she watched the lion from a distance, learning its every move. Each day she would set out a small amount of food for the lion before quickly returning to her hiding spot. Gradually, she was able to come closer and closer to the lion until she was able to sit almost beside him and watch him eat. Those terrible jaws that she so feared tore into the meat she had set out. Gathering all of her courage and staring timidly at the lion, she slowly reached out to stroke its chin. As she stroked, three whiskers fell into her hand. Delighted with this gift from the lion, she quickly made her way back to the wise man's home.

"I have the three whiskers. Now please make the love potion for me," she begged.

"You have no need for my potions, even if I could make them."

"But you promised you would make a love potion for me when I returned with the lion's whiskers!"

"No, I only promised I would help you. Return to Segab and your husband. You learned how to approach the lion… slowly. Do the same with Segab. The lion gave you a gift, though only a small one. So will Segab. Be as patient with your loved ones as you were with the lion you so feared. Only then will you learn to love each other."

The Fortune-Teller

Georges de La Tour

Georges de La Tour was born in France in 1593. His father was a baker. The scene painted here is typical of the time period in which he lived. Later, Georges de La Tour became an official painter for the court of the king of France.

Notice the fortune-teller's wrinkled but powerful face. She holds the young man's attention with her hands and her eyes. The faces of the other two women seem very bland in comparison. But look closely at their hands. What do you think is happening here?

Story-telling is an art. It has the power to hold its listeners when the tale is well told. But beware! As with anything you hear or read, it's important to question the sources of your information. Otherwise, you may find yourself, like this young gentleman, caught as a player in someone else's fortune!